Woofs of Wisdom:
A Tail of Rescue

by Megan Johnson and Amy Sturm
illustrated by Brooke O'Neill

For Tim—who inspired us
with the perfect song.
I miss you... we all do.

And to Doug, my shadow whose
love and forgiveness knows
no bounds.

And of course, Paul, who has
taught me the art of living quietly
in the moment.

~Megan Johnson

For my Dad—who encouraged
me to "use my head for something
besides a hat rack." Love you big!

For Norton—
my loyal & loving muse.

And also Monty, a.k.a. Monster,
for reminding me to take
life less seriously.

~Amy Sturm

Woofs of Wisdom: A Tail of Rescue ©
First Printing, 2020 in the
United States of America
Text and Art copyright © 2020
Megan Johnson and Amy Sturm

Choose Me
(Tim Johnson, Jody Gray)
© 1999 RMM 416 (SESAC), The Bigger They Are
Music (SESAC) admin by RMM 416 Publishing,
Reservoir Media Music (ASCAP), Smyth of Toons
(ASCAP) admin by Reservoir Media Music.
All rights reserved. Used by permission.

Can you find the bones hidden throughout
the book? You might be surprised by
where they are. Happy Hunting!

"In a perfect world every home would have a dog
and every dog would have home."

Hello and welcome to the Woofs of Wisdom Rescue Academy. Did you know that adopting or rescuing is a great way to give a dog a loving home?

Today I will give you a sneak peek into the Academy and what it REALLY means to be a rescue dog.

Let's get started!

Behind this doggie door it's all about
the human-dog connection.

Our lab assistants learn all they can about humans,
so they can find them their perfect pooch match.

Before the dogs can be adopted,
they must be trained.

You see, humans get so caught up in the hustle and bustle of everyday life, that they forget the simple things.

Our job is to remind them, in our own wise and wonderful ways, about the things that matter.

During training, each dog learns some important life lessons that they can later share with a human of their own.

Lessons such as...

Walk on the Wild Side
Remember to run, romp and play,
even in your own backyard.

Enjoy Quiet Moments
Rest, relax and embrace the silence.

Patience

Not all life lessons are easy ones! Patience is the ability to count down before you blast off...3.2.1 breathe.

Don't Let Others Define You
It's what's on the inside that counts.

Sit, Snuggle and Listen
Sometimes just being there is the greatest gift.

Dig for Buried Treasure

When life gets ruff, dig a little deeper—look beyond the surface, you may be surprised by what you might find.

Don't Bite
Avoid biting when a simple growl will do... Use your words!

We All Go Through the Same Stuff Differently

You may see a situation one way and a friend may see
it another. It's not about who's right or wrong.
It's about trying to see someone else's point of view.

Be Yourself
What makes you unique is what makes you awesome,
or as we like to say here at the academy; pawsome!

You are Stronger Than You Think
Life will throw you curveballs, for the record,
these aren't the ones we like to chase,
but you are both strong and brave, don't give up!

Love Unleashed
Don't hold back, love big and with all your heart.

Once training is complete, it's test time, which involves reciting the **Golden Drool**:

The rescued ones' needs will vary
but all will need a daily teaching
~OF~
PATIENCE, LOVE
& LOYALTY
I will not only be their teacher
but more importantly
I will be their
BEST FRIEND.

After learning the skills needed to rescue their person,
each dog heads out to his or her assigned shelter where they wait
to be "discovered" and Operation Choose Me begins.

So what happens
once a match
is made?

Well that's the easy part... a wag-worthy friendship
starts to grow, followed by a love that is lasting
and carefree; a special human-dog connection forms
around those two magic words....
CHOOSE ME!

This book belongs to _____
your name

and my furry hero _____ .
your dog's name

Place a photo or draw a picture of your furry friend.

Adoption Tips

- Have a family meeting to discuss what each member of the family can do to help with the care of the dog in their own way. It's important everyone is involved.

- Lifestyle and personality will dictate the size and type of dog. Ask shelter staff for guidance - they are experts at helping make the perfect match.

- Choose a type of dog whose energy level is equal to, or less than, your own.

- Be sure your rescue buddy is not left alone for long of periods of time, you are his whole world. Figure out how you can schedule your dog into your life.

- Don't overlook senior dogs, they need homes just as badly as cute puppies. They make wonderful companions for homes that are not as active.

- Set a schedule. What time will they eat? What time will you go for walks? Playtime? Also, who will help with each task?

- The dog will need time to settle in and relax. No dog is perfect. Remember that they have likely had a lot of changes in a short period, so they are probably a bit confused. They might be a little nervous at first (i.e. potty mishaps) but that will get better with love & patience.

- Socialization is key to a happy and confident dog.

- Clean up toys and stuffed animals off the floor and check the house for anything the dog might confuse as a toy. Remember a new puppy is like a baby, so make sure you create a safe and secure environment.

- Get to know your veterinarian right away, take your rescue buddy for a check-up, introduce him to the vet. If an emergency happens you have a veterinary partner which will give you confidence knowing who is helping your dog get well.

- Enjoy the process, your are emBARKing on a new adventure together with your new rescue buddy!

GIMLI

Chippy

norton

FIN

CASSIE

HUMPHREY

Trixie

DONUT

SALSA

BARNEY

SCRUFFY

LUCKY

BENJI

KLAUS

COOKIE

10% of the profits from the sale of this book will go to programs that support animal rescue.

CHASIN' our TALES

Checkout the song that inspired the book at www.chasin-our-tales.com

Megan Johnson is a mother of two human children as well as a plethora of various other species. Megan lives on a farm in Franklin, Tennessee and is a Realtor, a Horse Program Director for the County Agriculture Extension, and believes teaching children compassion for animals is a vital part of our well-being as a planet.

Amy Sturm is the mom of 2 boys, a school counselor and a wanna-be farm girl. She lives on 32 acres in Tennessee with her husband, pound pups and a collection of chickens. This is Amy's second children's book, she is also the author of, Cock-a-doodle Sue. Amy hopes Woofs of Wisdom will encourage others to visit their local animal shelter and perhaps find love at the end of a leash.

Brooke O'Neill is a graphic designer and illustrator who resides in the south-suburbs of Chicago. Currently she is living her dream of illustrating children's books and hanging out with her husband, two young children, and fur-child.

CPSIA information can be obtained
at www.ICGtesting.com
Printed in the USA
LVHW072027141020
668357LV00078B/544